# Specimen Sight-Reading Tests for Flute

Grades 1-5

**The Associated Board of the Royal Schools of Music**

# GRADE 1

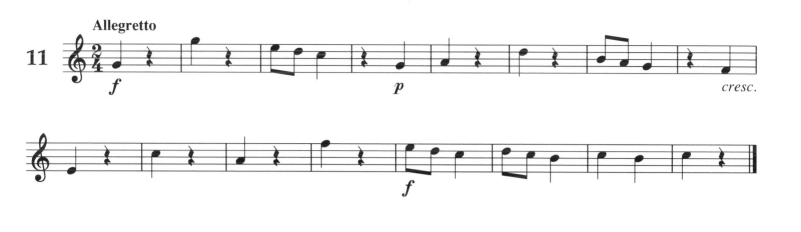

**14** Allegretto

**15** Andante

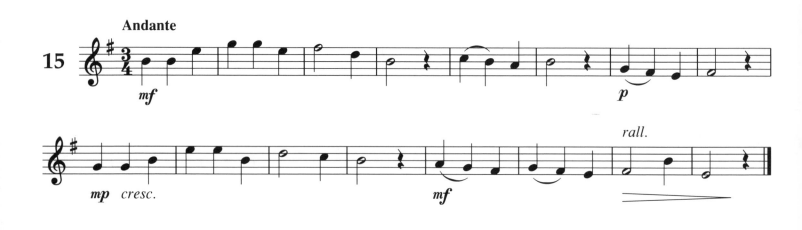

**16** Moderato

# GRADE 2

**Con moto**

4

**Lively**

5

**Andantino**

6

**Allegro**

7

# GRADE 3

# GRADE 4

# GRADE 5

Typeset by Musonix
Printed by Caligraving Limited, Thetford, Norfolk, England
AB 2466
6:01

Now you c
clarinet solo
recorded arrangement

jazz

# TAKE
## THE
# LEAD

## clarinet

IMP

**International**
**MUSIC**
**Publications**

International Music Publications Limited
Griffin House 161 Hammersmith Road London W6 8BS England

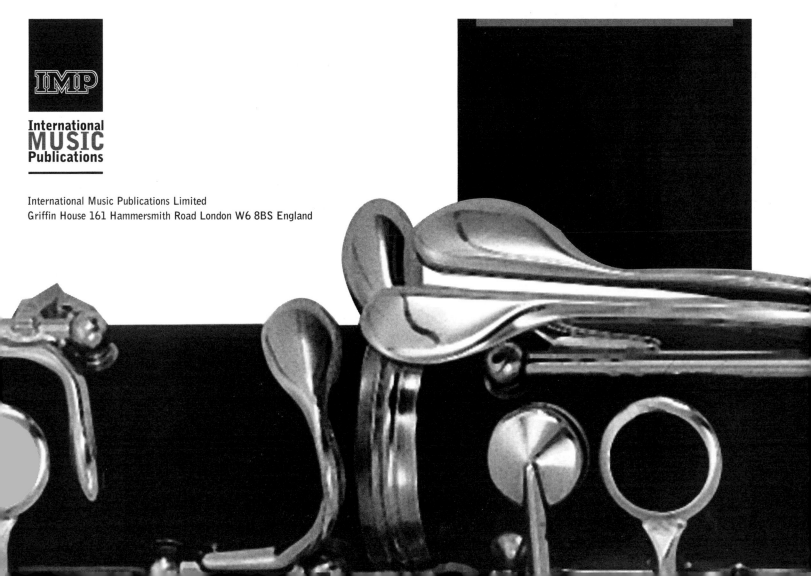

Series Editor: Sadie Cook

Editorial, production and recording: Artemis Music Limited
Design and production: Space DPS Limited

Published 1999

**International MUSIC Publications**

International Music Publications Limited

| | |
|---|---|
| **England:** | Griffin House<br>161 Hammersmith Road<br>London W6 8BS |
| **Germany:** | Marstallstr. 8<br>D-80539 München |
| **Denmark:** | Danmusik<br>Vognmagergade 7<br>DK1120 Copenhagen K |

*Carisch*

| | |
|---|---|
| **Italy:** | Via Campania 12<br>20098 San Giuliano Milanese<br>Milano |
| **Spain:** | Magallanes 25<br>28015 Madrid |
| **France:** | 20 Rue de la Ville-l'Eveque<br>75008 Paris |

clarinet

# TAKE
## THE
# LEAD

## In the Book...

# On the CD...

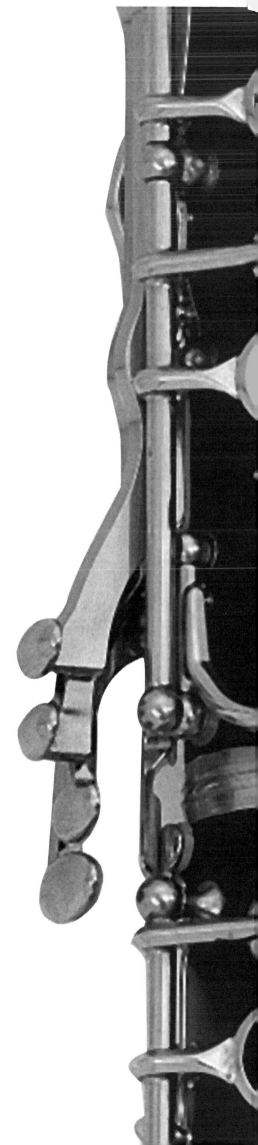

# Birdland

Demonstration

Backing

Music by
Josef Zawinul

# Desafinado

Words by Newton Ferriera de Mendonca
Music by Antonio Carlos Jobim

Demonstration    Backing

**Moderate Bossa Nova**

# Don't Get Around Much Anymore

Demonstration  Backing

Music by Duke Ellington

# Fascinating Rhythm

Demonstration    Backing

Music and Lyrics by
George Gershwin and Ira Gershwin

**Moderate Swing**

# Misty

Music by Erroll Garner

Demonstration    Backing

# My Funny Valentine

Music by Richard Rodgers

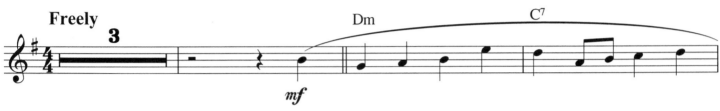

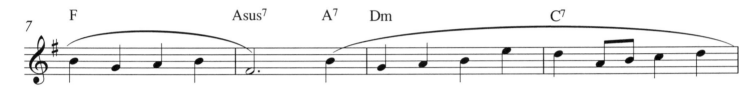

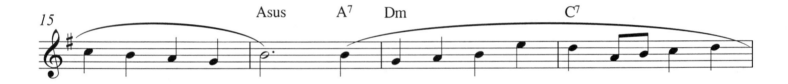

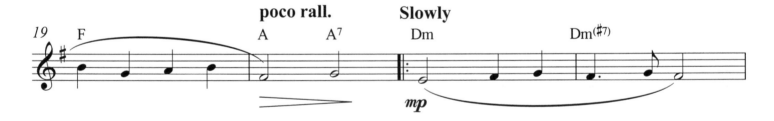

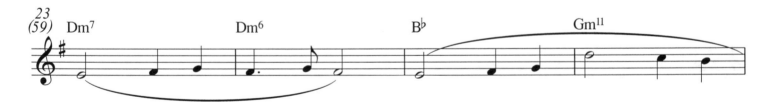

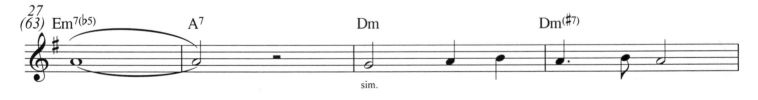

Demonstration  Backing

# One O'Clock Jump

Music by Count Basie

# Summertime

Music and Lyrics by George Gershwin,
Du Bose and Dorothy Heyward and Ira Gershwin

Demonstration · Backing

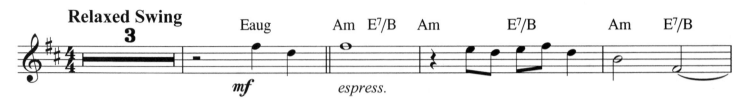

Reproduced and printed by
Halstan & Co. Ltd., Amersham, Bucks., England

# You can be the featured soloist with TAKE **THE** LEAD

Now you can be the feature clarinet soloist on eight specially recorded arrangements

## clarinet

### MOVIE HITS

**FEATURES**
- Full backings to play along with
- Full demonstration tracks to help you learn the songs
- Carefully selected and edited arrangements
- Chord symbols in concert pitch

## Collect these titles, each with demonstration and full backing tracks on CD.

| 90s Hits | Movie Hits | TV Themes | Christmas Songs | The Blues Brothers |
|---|---|---|---|---|
| **The Air That I Breathe** (Simply Red) | **Because You Loved Me** (Up Close And Personal) | **Coronation Street** | **The Christmas Song (Chestnuts Roasting On An Open Fire)** | **Sho Caught The Katy And Left Me A Mule To Ride** |
| **Angels** (Robbie Williams) | **Blue Monday** (The Wedding Singer) | **I'll Be There For You (theme from _Friends_)** | **Frosty The Snowman** | **Gimme Some Lovin'** |
| **How Do I Live** (LeAnn Rimes) | **(Everything I Do) I Do It For You** (Robin Hood: Prince Of Thieves) | **Match Of The Day** | **Have Yourself A Merry Little Christmas** | **Shake A Tail Feather** |
| **I Don't Want To Miss A Thing** (Aerosmith) | **I Don't Want To Miss A Thing** (Armageddon) | **(Meet) The Flintstones** | **Little Donkey** | **Everybody Needs Somebody To Love** |
| **I'll Be There For You** (The Rembrandts) | **I Will Always Love You** (The Bodyguard) | **Men Behaving Badly** | **Rudolph The Red-Nosed Reindeer** | **The Old Landmark** |
| **My Heart Will Go On** (Celine Dion) | **Star Wars (Main Title)** (Star Wars) | **Peak Practice** | **Santa Claus Is Comin' To Town** | **Think** |
| **Something About The Way You Look Tonight** (Elton John) | **The Wind Beneath My Wings** (Beaches) | **The Simpsons** | **Sleigh Ride** | **Minnie The Moocher** |
| **Frozen** (Madonna) | **You Can Leave Your Hat On** (The Full Monty) | **The X-Files** | **Winter Wonderland** | **Sweet Home Chicago** |
| Order ref: 6725A – Flute | Order ref: 6908A – Flute | Order ref: 7003A – Flute | Order ref: 7022A – Flute | Order ref: 7079A - Flute |
| Order ref: 6726A – Clarinet | Order ref: 6909A – Clarinet | Order ref: 7004A – Clarinet | Order ref: 7023A – Clarinet | Order ref: 7080A - Clarinet |
| Order ref: 6727A – Alto Saxophone | Order ref: 6910A – Alto Saxophone | Order ref: 7005A – Alto Saxophone | Order ref: 7024A – Alto Saxophone | Order ref: 7081A - Alto Saxophone |
| Order ref: 6728A – Violin | Order ref: 6911A –Tenor Saxophone | Order ref: 7006A – Violin | Order ref: 7025A – Violin | Order ref: 7082A - Tenor Saxophone |
| | Order ref: 6912A – Violin | | Order ref: 7026A – Piano | Order ref: 7083A - Trumpet |
| | | | Order ref: 7027A – Drums | Order ref: 7084A - Violin |